Flowers
Love
&
Other
Things

Nelson O. Ottenhausen

by
Nelson O. Ottenhausen

ISBN: 0-977372-3-2

Printed and Published
in the United States of America by
Trent's Prints
Chumuckla, Florida
www.trentsprints.com

To: _____

From: _____

Date: _____

"If you see someone
without a smile,
Give them one"!

"...Perhaps someone will remember, and it will make a difference.

Author: Unknown

This book is dedicated
in loving memory
to my son:

Karl M. Ottenhausen

Born September 12, 1958
Reborn April 3, 1996

The hand of God has chosen the hour
So, rest now forever your weary head
As you lie upon your final bed;
For it is within the Blessed power
To raise your spirit as He would a flower,
Absolving all the troubles which you have said.
Illusions are replaced with Truth instead
Of harboured fears and dour.
Cradle your soul in Father's hand
And receive His unfettered Love
So that you may now understand why
Life is everlasting in a heavenly land
By a promise from Him above;
The children of God will never die.

To Nelson, A Poet

Letters running into words
and then into emotions,
that until you put them down went totally unnoticed
to a world so desperately in need of what you have inside.
And, so you stopped,
and took the time to record what's on your mind,
viewpoints so uniquely yours,
seen through a poet's eyes.

Once locked away,
but now remembered,
giving cause to cry.
For without knowing what you do,
you record the acts,
that when combined,
make up life,
each leading to the next birth and death,
and love of life, all penned with such deep care.
Set upon a once blank page, as if belonging there.

And only when I read the lines, did I begin to comprehend
the depth of what a poet feels,
and shares through use of pen.
Through your eyes I began to see,
through your words I began to feel
a world that until this time, seemed distant and unreal.

And then I read your poetry, and began to understand
the thoughts and the emotions, penned with a poet's hands.

Wanda M. Argersinger

Creation

Man is not an artless Messiah
who has no inkling of his calling.

The art is to see
beyond oneself and learn
that destiny is not chaos,
but a well defined pattern of fate.

Listen to T. S. as he quotes the scriptures
in the attempt to reveal his truths,
and if you feel the need to add your own worth,
suck in your pride, release your passion
and spit out your creation
because one does not hear by silence.

Let good and evil fall where they may,
but choose wisely.
The whining discontent, the seekers of pity
and the self righteous hypocrite
will not be remembered nor revered.

Hold your rage and soften your denials.
It is not hysterical fury
nor incoherent protests that drive us.

But, if there is a fire in your belly
and if your visions are fervid, let them go.
Do not take them with you,
for a voice from the grave is never heard.

Nelson O. Ottenhausen

Table of Contents

Section One

Poems
of
Flowers

Along the Garden Path

If you have nothing better to see
come, take a walk along with me
amid the shaded oaks and other trees.

Watch sunbeams cascade through the forest crest
each showing a part of the earth's green breast,
lighting the surrounding rood.

Textured ferns with variegated leaves
cast shadows down within the trees—
this fairy tale garden has a calmness
of imposing magnitude.

Shaded blossoms in Cinderella grace
display the palettes of beauty's face
and presents a majestic interlude.

There, I sometimes like to stroll
to feel the warmth of softened earth beneath my sole.

We'll wander along the path of jade
as it meanders about in the cooling shade,
it creates such a peaceful mood.

Near the path, graceful plants and flowers
may captivate us with their delicate powers,
capturing our minds with a mystical servitude.

We can smell the fragrance of our blooming friends
with an intimate sense that does not end,
ourselves, lost in the solitude.

So now, if you have nothing better to see
come, take this walk along with me,
amid the shaded oaks and other trees.

A Flower

Nature's mystery
that grows
a flower

Is witness
to God's
almighty power.

Silent Beauty

Sometimes, words
have no power
to describe the sight
of a pretty flower.

Flowers

Of all the Nature's precious gifts,
born in early Spring,
I like flowers most of all
because of the joy they bring.

They boost morale,
they lift the spirit
with feelings beyond a reason.

They soothe the soul,
they please the eye
and announce the change of season.

A Flower of Spring

If I were to pick
a flower of spring,
I would choose
the lilac bloom.

Their wonderful colors
please the eye
and their fragrance
can fill a room.

Morning Glory

As darkness fades
by light of day,
painting the morning sky,
a movement of beauty
begins to happen
when a sunbeam passes by.

Miniature trumpets
unfurl their bell,
struck by the light of dawn,
hailing the world,
exposing their bloom,
with a slow deliberate yawn.

They greet the morning
with muted herald,
telling a silent story,
dressed in color,
dabbed with dew,
a flower—
the morning glory.

Glads

With sword like leaves
and spikes of flowers,
on long thick stalks of green,
whorls of blooms
in heavy clusters,
born to a single gene.

From subtle pinks
to torrid reds,
some over two feet tall;
the gladiolus,
a regal flower,
stands heads above them all.

Sweet Fragrance

Who can forget
the scent of a rose,
a gardenia
or jasmine in bloom.

Sweet blossoms
smother the foliage,
and attract the creators
to inhale their silent flume.

Beckoned by some primal call,
songs persist in the brain
to embrace the seductive fume.

But, all too soon,
we discover
there is no fragrance
to surpass
a woman's love.

The Daffodil

In a far away place not long from here
Is a small wooded knoll where the air is clear.
It stands alone on top of a hill,
Among the trees is the white daffodil.

The long green stem is straight and tall
As it stands so proud among them all,
In glorious color and oh so still,
Among the trees is the white daffodil.

The outstretched blossom of yellow and white
Beckons to all to behold this sight,
And to see in God's almighty will,
Among the trees is the white daffodil.

And now my love so you may see
This wondrous sight along with me,
Come dream with me on top of this hill,
Among the trees is the white daffodil.

Wild Flowers

In the beginning,
an evolution sweeps the land
and the wild flowers grow.

In the ground,
beautiful blooms carpet the earth
for nature's garden show.

In light,
colors woo the silent mate,
luring the unknown hosts.

In the air,
songs of fragrance ride the breeze
and drift like sailing ghosts.

In Fall,
unseen spirits soften the hue
and the petals start to dry.

In the end,
an evolution sweeps the land
and the wild flowers die.

Violets in the Snow

Sometimes, in the early days
after spring has just begun,
a subtle change of weather
may hide the warming sun.

A sudden storm of winter
covers a budding earth
with an inch or two of coldness
that hides the land's rebirth.

But, after the storm has passed
and the chill begins to wane,
life that grows is often exposed,
through a cold and frozen bane.

They peek from `neath a frost white veil,
flowers that struggle to grow—
the new born faces of shining purple
are violets in the snow.

The Rose

A natural metaphor of beauty;
elegant,
colorful,
fragrant,
even when standing alone.

Its bud or open bloom
is the diamond
among all flowered jewels.

Its image seduces the eye,
fondles the brain,
and enhances
the love of flesh and bone.

Its floral essence heightens emotions,
compels the soul
to look,
to smell,
to sing.

Sometimes to touch.

But remember, stroke
the slender stem softly,
for lest you forget,
a rose can also sting.

The Promise

The promise of God
is witnessed and heard,
in each blooming flower
and each singing bird.

Butterfly

Delicate petals
flutter past me,
and I am intrigued.

The intricate form
bounces on air
in unhurried flight
with colors of orange,
and blacks and white.

With no true course
the intoxicated blur
seems to have no way.

Yet, without prejudice,
this metamorphic insect
brings beauty to a summer's day.

Section Two

Poems
of
Love

Love

True love
comforts the soul,
frees the spirit
and makes
the earth move,
for all eternity.

The Heart

When the hands
of lovers touch,
the heart awakens.

It does not listen
to the mind,
nor to the tongue,
for the heart knows not
of what they speak.

The heart knows
only compassion,
understanding
and visions
of beauty
in all things.

It only knows love.

Day Dreams

You have touched me
in a special way,
with a smile,
with a word,
with a loving kiss.

You brighten my life
from within
with a thought,
with a dream,
with a fantasy.

My heart is filled
with happiness
because I know you care.

It will not end
for you and I,
for true lovers
never end a daydream

Silent Love

You stepped into my life,
unexpected,
and I loved you.

You know not
what is in my heart
nor on my mind,
and I cannot tell.

I have danced with you
a thousand times,
but we have never touched.

I have kissed you often,
yet our lips have never met.

Your smile sends me
into thoughts that are with me,
always.

You are my dream.
You are my fantasy.
You are my silent love.

Night Love

Come my sweet,
Sleep within my arms
and dream.

Dream the paramour
until the morning wakes.

Ecstasy

Like a whisper
on the evening wind,
her smile
brought me love
and my heart crashed.

I could not move,
I could not speak,
I could only enjoy
the moment.

Warmth,
washed over me
and I reached
the pinnacle of passion,
then was swept over the edge ...
screaming.

Things I know

Dear one,
there are things I know.

I know of your being,
I have held you.

I know of your mind,
my thoughts are there.

I know of your heart,
my spirit walks within it.

I know of your love,
you have given it to me.

I know of your soul,
for we are mated.

Dear one,
these are things I know.

A Friend

There is no need
for legal bonds,
nor spoken word,
nor ceremony
of any kind.

A friend does not condemn,
does not seek retribution,
nor point the finger of guilt.

A friend does not degrade,
but only praises
and expects no reward.

A friend gives without asking
and does not question.

A friend supports without cause
and does not judge.

To have a friend
is a blessing.
To be a friend,
is divine love.

Section Three

Other Things

Prayer

When uttered,
a single prayer in darkness
becomes the light
of but one candle.

A multitude
becomes the sun.

Little Things

They are born
in many ways
and with many shapes.
Some are fuzzy,
some are furry
and some are wrinkled.

Some of them even have wings.

Ahhh...but wait,
this one's different.
It has arms and legs
and a beautiful smile.

But alas,
it's still
just one of those...
little things.

The Owl and The Eagle

Birds of prey
the owl and the eagle,
one by night,
the other by day.

At night,
the Prince of Darkness
glides on muted flight,
seeking the sounds
of survival.

By day,
the Emperor of the Sky
soars to a majestic height
to claim his realm.

The owl and the eagle—
brothers on the wind.

I

Many things an i can be.

It can be a vowel
and change itself
as a chameleon
to become part of a noun or verb.

Often, it can hide in prepositions
or even in an adverb.

An eye can have shape,
it can have form,
it can ogle, leer and stare.

It can have many colors
and look almost anywhere.

Sometimes, it may even be bloodshot.

An eye can be an obstacle
to stop a camel
from jumping through a needle.

It can be a window
to see into a man's soul.

An I can be something
that stands alone
to perform its own role.

But, of all the things an i can be
I like best the I that's me.

Seasons

Through evolution,
the four seasons blend
together in a continuum
of solar chronology.

Linked together,
as a circled chain,
never ending in time,
through evolution.

Sweet Destiny

While shades of winter lurk in the woodland shadows,
a new sun born's life
as Spring unfolds a floral pattern
from an eternal blueprint.

Delicate perfumes whisper sweetness to the air
as the eye inhales a fire storm of color,
engulfing the pregnant earth
with a brilliant beauty of birth.

Then, at the pinnacle of glory, destiny prevails
and evolution transforms the story;
thus, passes all things
and only a remembrance remains.

Spring

The winter's days begin to warm
as the sunlight starts to grow,
shining more and more each day,
melting the cold white snow.

Dark clouds turn to puffy white,
billowing up to touch the sky,
bringing a peace and serenity,
that's pleasing to the eye.

Soft warm breezes and gentle rains,
start nature's call for rebirth,
the annual time for awakening
has aroused the dormant earth.

The crocus, the tulips and daffodils bloom,
spreading shoots beyond their cyme,
showing their colored flowers
because they know it's time.

The plants and trees respond in kind
to turn their foliage green,
bursting forth, eager with life,
so spring can now be seen.

Summer

A brilliant sun
bears on the land
and dissolves a dormant spring,
It suppresses the rains
and the essence of life they bring.

Veiled Images, born in the heat,
ride on a cushion of air,
shimmering on the horizon,
and appear to go nowhere.

Oppressed by swelter and heavy heat,
life cannot prevail,
time slows down to a gradual crawl
through a steamy fog-like veil.

The kindred spirit of nature's born,
cannot survive the blaze,
only shade offers welcome relief
from the torrid, scorching days.

Summer's Mirage

Brilliant rays of sunlight,
cause a wavy sight to appear,
on a far and distant horizon,
that always seems so near.

Dancing above the hard baked ground,
they ride the shimmering earth,
they float along on a separate path
that creates a sense of worth.

But, the vision is false and not what it seems
as it tricks the perceiving eye,
this kindred spirit of substans truth
is not but a bold face lie.

The view is one of nature's tricks,
of things that aren't really there,
an image of magic, latent ghosts
on the hot dry summer air.

Summer Storm

Out on the distant horizon,
racing across the sky,
spreads a pool of grayish black,
where nature has gone awry.

Flashes of brilliant lightening,
streak through an ominous cloud,
rumbles of rolling thunder,
announces the storm out loud.

A thunderhead, soars to the heavens,
its top a rose pink hue,
riding along a column of air,
where the sky is a brilliant blue.

The spectrum arrives in a long gray line,
driving rain with a tempest force,
a squall, with bolts of crashing light,
drenches the earth in its course.

After the rains and violent winds,
when the storm has passed us by,
the air returns to stillness
and a rainbow spans the sky.

Melodies of the Rain

With a gentle rain
comes the sound of white.

Its steady flow
calms me
like a children's lullaby.

The hypnotic cadence
wraps around my thoughts
and purges the loneliness
from my mind.

I am captured
by the spell,
and it consoles me.

Soon, I sense the tempo
and the rhythm,
soft and clear;
they are the verse,
they are the songs,
they are the melodies of the rain.

Autumn

The stage is set for autumn's show,
the days are warm and mellow,
fall is nature's softening time,
turning trees to gold and yellow.

With dazzling hues of reds and amber,
are browns and shades of heather,
gracing the hardwoods of sturdy oaks,
embracing the autumn weather.

The awesome sight of all the colors,
painted for us to behold,
standing against a brilliant sky,
are trees of shining gold.

Then on a day the trees respond,
to nature's mysterious call,
shedding their dying foliage,
the leaves begin to fall.

At last, the leaves have all come down,
and the branches are clean and clear,
autumn lies resting upon the ground,
to be born again next year.

Leaves of Gold

When the season morning wakes
dressed in a frost white gown,
summer's life, rich and green
soon begins to brown.

But, somewhere between
are sights beyond belief,
spectacular dazzling colors
as autumn paints each leaf.

The foliage turns more brilliant
with the passing of each day,
it reaches a final color
then breezes blow it away.

Life is over now,
winter brings on the cold,
but I shall always remember
the autumn leaves of gold.

Ghosts of Autumn

I have seen
the ghosts of autumn
during Indian Summer days,
these will o'the wisps
have shape and form
and appear as a smoky haze.

They rise above
the smoldering fire
and mingle
throughout the trees.
They rustle the dying foliage
as they dance
among the leaves.

The smoke you see
is the spirit of spring,
released by the fires of fall,
that leaves a corpse
of ashes,
to be covered
by winter's pall.

Season's Change

The last hot breeze of summer
burnishes the leaves
and the season slips away.

Colors of gold and crimson
ooze through the green
and autumn is magic,
but only for a little while.
Soon, a raging chill casts
the colors to the ground
and the adolescence of June is gone.

Spent like a shriveled corpse,
dried and burnt,
they lie beneath the living host,
waiting for their coffin of white.

Year's end is almost here.

Winter

The blustery days of fall are here,
the trees are black and bare,
dew upon the ground is frost
and a dampness fills the air.

As evening falls, clouds roll in,
laden with frosty snow,
creating a sense of darkness
as a northern begins to blow.

Gusty winds are winter cold,
they swirl the snow around,
dancing with each little snow flake
before it touches the ground.

A blanket of snow, covers all,
in a silent coat of white,
falling gently, still and quiet
through the long and chilly night.

In the early morning dawn,
a magic has been performed,
a season has changed its colors
and my world has been transformed.

Now, I feel the passion,
of hope as I dream of spring,
when the season changes color
and warmth that it will bring.

Awakening

First light creeps in from the east
and darkness steals away unseen;
while cold damp air haunts the black horizon,
night ghosts linger across a moonbeam.

The last strains of the nightingales
still echo in the trees
as morning birds cast
their first voice into the warming breeze.

Dawn born's a new day
and the sun slips its darkened womb.

Mothers, adorned with young,
silence hungry cries with nipples,
laden heavy with sweet milk.

Flowers unfurl to herald the day
with silent tribute, sowing their scent
to the wind and daylight goes into full bloom.

Once again, life is not a darkened dream.

Daybreak

Out of the darkness
comes the dawn
and the blackness fades away,
turning the night of shadows
into a hazy gray.

Gently at first,
then boldly it comes,
with ever growing light.
Suddenly, all the gray is gone
as the sun comes into sight.

Sunset

The setting sun
is a wondrous sight,
that begins the dusk
and starts the night.

The western sky
shows pinks and blue,
with shades of orange
and a purple hue.

The red ball sun
finally slips away,
behind the horizon
and ends the day.

Evening Shade

Sunset paints
an oro ribbon
across the waters
as purple folds
onto the scene
and shadows etch
into the moon side of day.

Light dips under
and the evening shade
sails the buttress valleys
of majestic purple,
as wings of black fly in
to hide the gray.

A swan's song
echoes the nocturne
as the flame fades,
the eyes of darkness open
and evening shade passes away.

Night Tones

At sunset,
lavender surrounds the shaded trees,
dilutes the daylight
and twilight envelopes the land.

Evening creeps in
to introduce the overture
and dusk begins
the night melodies.

The nocturne sings
as shadows sound,
crickets chirp,
katydids reverberate
and cicada buzz in tune.

Tree frogs harmonize
their croaks into the fray,
and beckon their mates
to love the night away.
Often, you'll hear
an melody of a loon.

After moonrise,
shadows drift by,
then melt like echoes
into the blackness
as they pierce
the mirror of a lunar beam.

Whippoorwills
call their mournful strain,
and we pray that life
is not but a sad dream.

Inside the mantle of darkness,
nighthawks ride the black thermals
while fuzzy bull bats create eddies
through the darkened currents,
lending their chit-chit to the ode.

A midnight baritone
glides in on silent wings,
horns on a feathered helmet
with talons of death
clutched upon a furry load.

The great owl hoots
and the symphony of night plays on.

When morning comes,
center stage brightens
and gray light seeps in;
then for a moment,
but, only for a moment
all is quiet at dawn.

The night tones end
and daylight is another poem.

Beaches

A sea breeze tames the summer air
where sand and water meet,
blowing in from out at sea
it cools the mid-day heat.

Salt air rises along the shores,
floating to the inland bays,
like a shrouded ghost it softens the sun
in a light and misty haze.

Shore birds race a rushing tide
as the sea rolls over the land,
draining away as quick as it came
washing down the snow white sand.

Sea oats nod on stems of gold
that grow on a windswept dune,
swaying gently back and forth
slow dancing without a tune.

On the Beach

Stroll a beach on a mid-summer's day,
revel in its solitude,
relinquish your thoughts of troubled times
and absorb the surrounding mood.

Hear the laugh of flying gulls
soaring the sandy turf,
listen to the tinkle of tiny shells
that roll in a foaming surf.

Watch the waves of rolling thunder
that quickly run up the shore
then, just as fast they return to the sea,
to come rolling in once more.

Taste the salt in the blowing breeze
and soak yourself in the sun,
languish your mind in this peaceful quest,
to relax and just have fun.

Ocean Spray

Rolling seas
begin to swell,
wind sweeps o'er a wave,
riding an edge
of a salty crest,
surfing the leeward nave.

A streak of mist
blows across the top
as a shower of ocean spray,
to the siren songs
of sea nymphs,
out where the dolphins play.

Waterfall

Liquid thunder
spills
from a mountain wall,
a waterfall,
crashes to earth.

From towering peaks
of breathless height,
a frothy white
curtain cascades down,
to create birth.

Amid the roar,
a silent splendor,
easy to see
in nearby trees,
spirits
that twist and swirl.

Above the basin pool
hangs a ghost like shroud
with rainbows
in its curl.

From afar,
an awesome view
and a
reverent sight,
etched in the mind forever.

Predator

Unseen, he approaches
the turf of the unsuspecting.

He circles,
hiding in the backdrop,
testing the scene,
looking for prey.

He picks up the scent
and chooses his quarry.

He moves in,
cautious,
slow,
deliberate—
the tools of conquest honed
to a razor's edge.

Closer,
ever closer.

Gliding through obstacles
he cuts off the retreat of the intended,
ready to strike.

Lips part,
blood pulsates through the veins
and primeval anticipation
floods the brain.

Now, the final moment
and the hunter reaches out
to the hunted.

"Wanna dance?"

Bristlecones

Oh tell me tall tree
with bristlecones,
what is your secret?

Why do your branches
not pass the seasons
as the oak and maple do?

What is the force
that spat you out
and keeps you forever green?

Oh tell me tall tree
with bristlecones,
what is your secret?

The Process

Thoughts begin
to battle with words.
Cramming, slamming, ramming
themselves into verse.
Everything flows through the gray.

Faster than the hand can move,
similes are slashed,
metaphors mauled,
and unfit words are wrestled away.

More words tumble askew
like flying chips,
whittled away with naught
into the pile of the forlorn.

The carving continues,
a phrase takes shape,
and a poem is born.

Somewhere in the poets mind,
it's got to be madness.

A Trilogy

There are some who call them shiftless,
some call them neer-do-wells
while others call them foolish.

But those who write the trilogy of the mind,
of the heart and of the soul,
call themselves poets.

Broken Feather

Trampled and forgotten,
an eagle feather lies broken
in the dust.

Did it fall with dignity
or did it fall in shame?

Was it worn in battle
by a proud name?
Perhaps by a painted warrior
or a mighty chieftain.

Is it the sign of a broken
promise, a broken spirit
or just a molt?

Does it matter?

For all that remains
is a broken feather,
trampled and forgotten.

The Universe

Somewhere,
far beyond the stars
in the endless depths of space,
a process of evolution stirs
not of the human race.

A vast abyss
of worlds and suns,
of gasses and stellar dust,
continues to change,
expanding with time,
and without constraints
it must.

Whether
this happened
by chance or plan,
no one knows for sure,
but somewhere,
out beyond the stars,
time is just a blur.

Being

In the soul
a human spirit,
in the heart
a human feeling.

In the mind
a human dream,
in the body
a human being.

Cosmos

Celestial bodies enrich our heavens,
faint spectrals of shimmering light,
constellations of distant worlds
in the depths of eternal night.

Their sprinkled pattern appears to be random
on the black dome of our sky.
But, there's order in this geography
and only God knows why.

Evolution

Birth,
the way of all things,
our fate sealed
in an envelop of time.

When it is revealed,
our destiny is passed
onto the way of all things,
death.

Picket Fences

Shoulder to shoulder
On dress parade,
Perfectly lined by command.

Silent sentinels,
Standing proudly,

Guarding the lords of the land.

The Change

Last night,
dreams turned up in my bed
and slipped unnoticed
into my brain.

Then and now
became a blend of one
as they tumbled
through the hour glass.

The grains mixed,
the joy and sorrow
were both pleasing
and annoying.

Fear and courage
were both one and the same,
with crying and laughter
sounding alike.

I felt confused
with a clearness
I had never sensed before,
but now I know
that warmth
is not just light alone.

Section Four

Only for the Lonely

Haiku

Black clouds bring the rain
that moistens the dry parched earth-
Now, I walk in mud.

Poetry

We all seek our destiny.

Those without despair
and restless spirits,
soar through life,
fulfilling their hopes and dreams.

Others challenge,
"Who do you think you are?
How dare you step
beyond the corn fields."

Others just cry alone.

I, on the other hand,
celebrate the peace
of simple things
and read poetry.

A Child

All humans born are not of Faust.
Many are born to the humanities,
some to the sciences,
while others are born to the arts.

Vocation matters little,
but there is always hope
that the kernel of the nut
expresses the nature of the tree.

As parents, we live a dream,
a nightmare or some combination of both,
but always, we live on the cusp
of a child's way.

Those who plan conception
do so for greatness.
It is not our fault if life disappoints us.
And often we wonder—
Is there reciprocity
when the kinship sours?

Perhaps in growing older
we may outlive what is not liked.
We can only hope.

The Search

We are self-ordained to search for something.
Sometimes we do so in the past,
sometimes we do so in the future,
but seldom do we do so in the present—
For that is where everything happens.

We fill our brains with clatter
of past regrets and future fantasies,
yet we rarely see the countryside,
the ruts in the road or nature in the now—
For that is where everything happens.

We are not always aware of the trees,
of the flowers or that we even breathe.
We pay little heed to our immediate existence
and remove ourselves from the moment of living—
For that is where everything happens.

Whatever passage we chose to lose ourselves
from our true being, it will always remain
as a fingerprint on our destiny and someday
it will become clear that we are always at the beginning—
For that is where everything happens.

The Old Barn

Standing beside a country road
is a barn that's old and gray,
serene and quiet in a rural field,
showing use, but no decay.

Its sturdy boards are streaked with paint
and traces of white washed lime,
mixed with red and other colors,
eroded by sun and time.

Long abandoned and empty,
weather beaten by storms and rain,
proud and stalwart in idle silence,
waiting to serve again.

Broken Union

Lying in the dust
are unused fragments
of marital dreams
scattered among pieces
of shattered hopes and happiness.

What power polluted the caring?

No matter,
the heart was hardened
by unkept vows
and cries out for vengeance
while compassion decays
like dried bones.

Part of the whole
is gone,
love is dead
and there is no pleasure
in a half made bed.

Why Do They Go

They step into your life
sudden and unexpected.

They bring happiness
and joy,
so you're glad they came.

They show they care
with gifts you'll treasure always.

And after they go,
the good times
fade into memories
and linger
in the mind
like ghostly shadows.

So you ask,
Is love broken?

One

When man and woman go beyond
the boundaries of themselves,
and into the sanctuary of each,
there is union.

And, if that union fails,
the fractured promises
must be swept aside and forgotten.

There is a great loneliness in one,
but there is solace
that no other condition can fulfill.

Expressions may be made
without rebuke,
without rebuttal
and without remorse.

Emotions can be open,
esteem may be whatever
is self pleasing and rejection
does not exist.

Alone, the spirit renews itself,
the soul mends
and the wounded heart begins to heal.

And so, seek no vengeance,
face the light of all things,
smile
and walk away.

Destiny

What is Destiny?

We are all born
to live and die
within some fragment of eternity.

But must it be so brief?

There is not much time to a person's life,
nor is there much time
to crate a legacy.

Why must it go so fast?

While on this earth,
too many of us search for a heaven,
only to discover there's a hell.

Are those our choices?

Perhaps.

Does one's destiny
depend on deeds?

I must learn to overcome the flames.

Unfaithful

You have not
broken my spirit,
only my heart.

You have not
weakened my resolve,
only my trust.

You have not
destroyed
my hopes,
my dreams
nor my aspirations,
only my patience.

I will survive.

Why

I hear you,
but there is no sound
in my ears.

I see you,
but there is no image
in my eyes.

I feel you close to me,
but I cannot touch you.

My heart says
you care for me,
but my mind
tells me it lies.

Your last sweet kiss
tasted bitter
and love became fouled
by the odor of death.

My soul cries out,
but there are no tears.

Renewal

If your hopes and dreams
are dashed by life,
and if you are afraid
to start again,
do not despair.

"How will I mend
the anguish of my soul
and redeem
life's happiness?"
you ask.

It is easy.

Repent from the heart
and spit the gall
from your lips.

Life

As I am born,
so am I dying
and every moment ages me.

My life
is but a breath of air
in a minute segment
of eternity.

When life is given,
it may also be taken
and sometimes
does so without a word.

"Why is that?" I ask.

I wait,
but the silence
to the question
could be so long,
I fear the answer
may never be heard.

Memories

Memories are but footprints
of history in the mind
and as I browse their course,
I find a potpourri of images.

Many are good,
Some are bad,
many are clear,
and some are vague.

All are welded to my brain.

Pleasant thoughts of the past
bring warm afterglow's;
a deed well done,
family members,
children
and good friends.

Others thoughts haunt my soul
with terror
and are better left unsaid.

Fadeout

Late in an autumn evening,
while daylight lingers,
the fading campfire glows
like a setting sun.

Close to the inferno's heart,
charred oak pieces lay,
bearing witness
to the searing flame.

The night air stirs
and the dying embers
show life once more.

But soon,
the breeze begins to ebb
and the transformation
to black continues.

Days

I love the dawn,
yet curse the light,
another day is taken from me.

I cannot hold back the sun
nor moon, nor stars,
they move to their own.

I cannot stop the sands
of the hourglass,
for it falls between my aging hands.

I cannot silence the ticks
of nature's clock,
for I know not where it is,
yet I feel its vibrations always.

I love the dawn,
yet curse the light,
another day is taken from me.

Prairie

The prairie land,
where grasses once bent
like waves
of the seven seas.

Now, they are sown
with concrete,
wheat and corn.

Do they yearn
for the untamed buffalo
of the past?

Or does their silence
mean they have accepted the plow?

The Beginning and the End

Nothing,
as in the beginning.

A holocaust of the void
and genesis becomes a universe,
thus,
everything.

Everything,
as in the end.

A holocaust of the universe
and genesis becomes a void,
thus,
nothing.

Call of the Past

When fraught with trouble, pain and ailment;
and with winter's season closing,
fear not if memory serves but the distant past.

Take solace from the echoes and feel their warmth.
Keep them close to your heart and make them last.

They are the magical strands to yesteryear;
to another time,
to another place,
to another world.

The Last Season

Flowers satisfy the perception
of respect before the velvet draped bier
and now, the meaning
of being is to console.

Just as the last sunbeam lures the eye
and illuminates the Spirit,
a symphony to the Host
will soothe the soul.

Mankind's innermost disposition
is to delay mortality
and linger in the Autumn of life,
for whatever the reason.

For some, it is but a brief moment,
for others a very long while;
however, somewhere just before eternity,
Nature's silent dictate
transforms the season.

Passing

Souls are taken from us
   every moment,
    every second,
     every hour of the day.

Fathers, mothers, sisters, brothers
   husbands, wives, friends and lovers,
all succumb to the final abstraction —
It is Nature's way.

Everything appears to be lost
but, nothing is really gone.

It is all still here
   in the mind,
    in the heart
     and in the spirit.

Life goes on.

Full Circle

Morning breaks and the sun climbs
over the horizon.
Nothing is different,
there is only more light.

With daylight comes the arc.

It grows and stretches out,
out to the edge of touch,
out to the edge of sound
and out to the edge of sight.

Secrets abound within the arc
and outsiders do not belong.

And when the arc comes full circle,
I smile, knowing the last blessing
will be said
by a priest in Jockey shorts.

The Creed

A soldier hunts.
And so too, the hunted
is a warrior,
each sworn to duty in time of peril.

With violence, the peace is shattered.
A heart is ruptured,
a spirit is torn,
and a soul is ripped
from human bondage.

The soldier watches,
as the fallen warrior's stain
seeps into the soil.

The soldier remembers then—
The Creed.
Defend the sacred Land;
Close with the enemy
and destroy those who would defile it;
Lay down one's own life
to keep the homeland free.

But the soldier is not at home.
He is on another's land,
the warrior's land,
and an oath of death has been fulfilled.

The soldier looks down upon the warrior
and a virtue leaves him.
He turns and leaves,
feeling not
a better man for what is done.

Homecoming

Today's happening
is anchored
to yesterday's experiences
and we all come home.

Relatives and friends
mourn their loss
as the soul is laid to rest.

Comfort without pain,
pleasure without sensation,
insight without seeing,
and peace will be absolute.

Darkness is now an eternal friend,
the sod an eternal cover
and the seasons evolve no more.
I have come home.

After the Battle

Lying fallow in unfurrowed row,
asleep the dead of the day.
Strong brave men, still and quiet,
soldiers of the blue and gray.

Their conflict no longer rages.
Fallen heroes one and all.
No longer will they rise again
to answer the battle's call.

They fought for what they believed,
not thinking it sacrifice
but, only of honor and duty
regardless of the final price.

As darkness entombs the silent field
it cools the blood stained sod
the deeds are done, the battle fought
and the souls belong to God.

Hallowed Ground

The tomb enfolds a fallen hero
and what once was, is not,
and we mourn.

Inscribed pylons honor the spirit,
enrich the memory
and we're forlorn.

Pain and suffering do not fill the void
as Father takes the soul
and we grieve.

Patriot songs ride the wind
as Mother Earth receives
and soon, we leave.

Life, A Summary

As we are born, so are we dying.
As we begin, we look ahead.
As we grow up, we look down.
As we grow old, we look back.
And when we become feeble,
we remember none of this.

And so we go on,
on to where we were always meant to go,
where nothing happens, or ever will.

Sometimes

Sometimes when it's cloudy,
sometimes rain will fall,
sometimes heavy,
sometimes light,
sometimes not at all.

Section Five

Short Stories

Spanish Moss

by Nelson O. Ottenhausen

Born and raised in northwestern Illinois, I had never seen Spanish Moss, except in pictures, until I came to the South in 1962, assigned to Fort Benning, Georgia for Army Officer's Infantry Training as a second lieutenant. The first sight of those clumps of grayish-green fiber hanging down from the tree limbs made such an impression on me that years later when I moved to Gulf Breeze, Florida, I felt compelled to write a poem about them, but it wasn't an easy thing to do.

For months I struggled to find the right words to express what I wanted to say about Spanish Moss—it's actually not a moss, but an epiphyte (Tillandsia usneoides). I searched various encyclopedias, dictionaries and every source I could think of for information, collecting three and a half pages of notes. I constantly sorted over the words I'd gathered, trying to glean out something to capture the spirit of what I wanted to say, but nothing jelled.

Often, I would ponder my impasse while on my daily walks around the Gulf Breeze area, searching my brain for the right words and phrases for the poem, trying to put together some satisfactory poetic structure, and debating with myself if I should compose it as a sonnet, a rhyming quatrain or just stanzas of open free verse. One day, I happened to change my usual walking route, and for the first time I went down the alleyway behind the old Food World store, now Office Depot, in the Live Oak Village Mall. There I discovered masses of Spanish Moss hanging in live oak trees in the wooded area just east of the mall. At the same time I found a small oak tree at the very end of the alley with moss hanging down far enough for me to touch.

Every day for the next two weeks I would stop at the little tree, hold a strand of moss in my hands and twist it, feeling its texture, looking up at it, hoping something would kick in and give me an idea about how to begin the poem. But all the while, nothing worthy came to mind.

Occasionally, during these stops, I would notice a man looking down at me from one of the third floor windows in the Soundings, a townhouse complex across the alley behind the mall overlooking the Santa Rosa Sound to the south. One day, while I stood looking at a strand of moss in my hand, the man came out of the building, crossed the alley and stopped about twenty feet from me, then shouted out, "Excuse me, sir. Can I ask you something?"

I replied, "Sure thing. What is it?"

He paused for a moment, quickly looked around, then continued with, "Well, I've been watching you come by here for the last two weeks now, and what I'd like to know is, just what is it that you got goin' with that tree?"

His unexpected question surprised me, and my mind went completely blank. After a second I recovered my senses and said, "I come here to stroke the moss on this tree to get inspired." I don't think he heard the rest of my explanation, the part about, "I've been trying to write a poem about Spanish Moss and needed to get some insight about how it felt," because he had abruptly turned and scurried away after my first sentence.

I never walked that route again.

A week after the incident, quite suddenly from out of nowhere, the poem came to me, and within minutes, I had exactly what I wanted.

Spanish Moss

In forests of cypress
and sturdy oaks,
hanging in southern trees,
are pendant ghosts
of shadows,
that sway to a gentle breeze.

Curly strands
twist and turn,
dangle as untatted lace,
a pallid green
with a tint of gray,
add a touch of charm and grace.

A Day at the Beach

by Nelson O. Ottenhausen

On the last Saturday in September, during my first year living in Florida, a lady friend and I headed out to Pensacola Beach to relax and "catch a few rays." We arrived about mid-morning, parked the car, and for two hours, we casually walked the snow-white beaches along the Gulf of Mexico, working up an appetite. A little before noon, we decided to grab a bite to eat, ending up at Peg Leg Pete's – now one of my favorite watering holes, located just west of the main drag on the Ft. Pickens road.

Since the weather was exceptional that day, we elected to eat our lunch in the open air and took a table on the porch outside the restaurant. My lady friend sat down facing the street while I sat looking out towards the inlet water behind her. I noticed only one other couple sitting outside with us, but they were on the other side of the porch.

After a few moments, a pretty, young waitress came and took our order, a pitcher of beer and two burger baskets with fries. I guessed her age to be somewhere around that of a junior or senior in college, but no later than her mid-twenties. When she left I casually watched her walk back to the restaurant for a bit, pre-assessing the amount of her tip.

Next, I glanced out at the water over my lady-friend's shoulder and noticed six young Brown Pelicans perched close together on six wooden pilings, those obtrusive tar encrusted posts used for mooring boats and constructing docks along waterfronts. I could tell the birds were juveniles by their grayish-brown body plumage, a shade or two lighter than an adult pelican's dark brown feathers, and by the short bluish head fuzz that makes their bulging eyes look like little black buttons.

From the moment I saw them I thought they all appeared to be staring directly at me, so I said to my lady friend, pointing behind her, "Look at those pelicans, they're staring at me."

Without turning around she snipped, "They're not staring at you."

I answered back with, "They are too. Take a look."

A second later, the waitress arrived, set down a pitcher of beer and two frosty mugs, smiled at me, then left. At the same time, my lady friend shot a quick glance over her left shoulder, turned back to me and rattled off, "Don't you know that a flock of pelicans all face the same way when they're perched on something or when they're standing on the ground? It's instinct."

"Yeah, yeah, yeah," I said. "I've heard it all before, but that's not the point. I tell you, those goofy things are staring at me. And look at their expression, it's kinda sad, don't you think?"

"Shut up and drink your beer. They're not sad. Birds can't be sad, especially pelicans."

I stopped watching the pelicans and began watching the waitress on her return trip back into the restaurant, still assessing the tip I would give her, so what I said next I thought was far enough under my breath that my lady friend couldn't hear. "They are too."

"I heard that."

"Heard what?"

"What you just said."

"I didn't say anything."

"Yes, you did."

"I did not."

"You did."

Again, I thought what I said was low enough that she couldn't hear. "Did not."

"I heard that, too."

"What?"

"You know what."

"No, I don't know what."

She leaned across the table towards me and half whispered, "Just be quiet now."

"I thought you were partially deaf."

"Only in one ear, but you're talking loud enough to wake the dead."

"I am not."

"You are, too."

"Am not."

"You are. Now be still. Here comes the waitress with our food."

I remained silent while the waitress served our order, all the while smiling at her and she smiling back at me. When she left, I again watched her until she entered the restaurant, still assessing her tip. Then I began to quietly eat my burger and chomp down a few fries. After a few mouthfuls, I took a quick peek at the goofy six and saw them still looking my way, still perched on the pilings.

I leaned over towards my lady friend and said, "They're still staring at me."

"Stop being so paranoid and finish your food. And, stop looking at those pelicans. They're not staring at you."

"Yes, they are. I'll bet they're staring at me because they're hungry."

"No, they're not."

"They are, too."

"Look, if you don't stop yappin' about those damn birds, I'm gonna move to another table."

"All right. All right. I'll be quiet."

We ate the rest of our meal without another word. When we finished, I paid the waitress our bill, giving her a substantial tip and a big smile, not only because she gave us what I thought was exceptional service, but also because her assessments rated very high on my criteria list. I rose up from the table, took a quick look around and started to leave, and at that exact moment, I noticed the sign on the screen door leading into the restaurant directly behind where I sat. Like a flash, it came to me, the explanation for the staring pelicans.

On the way home, my lady friend asked, "What are you grinning about?"

"Nothing."

"I'll bet it's about that pretty little waitress, isn't it?"

"No, not at all."

"You're old enough to be her father, maybe even her grandfather."

"It's not about her."

"I saw you give her a big tip."

"I only gave her a few bucks."

"Liar. You gave her a ten. And, that's not all you gave her."

"Whadda you mean?"

"I saw you ogle her."

"I did not ogle."

"Yes, you did."

"Did not."

"You did, too. You're a dirty old man."

"I am not."

"You are, too."

"I never even gave her a second thought."

"Then tell me what you were grinning about."

"Okay, I'll tell you. I know why those young pelicans were staring at me."

"Are you gonna start up about them damn birds again?"

"No, but really, I know why they were staring at me."

"I'm telling you, they weren't staring at you."

"Well, technically, you're right. They really weren't staring at me per sé."

"Thank God, you've finally come to your senses."

I said nothing for the remainder of the five-minute trip home to Gulf Breeze, but upon arriving at the condo, I penned the following poem.

Seaside Bar & Grill

Shoeless pelicans
perched atop mooring posts,
their mournful gaze
affixed to the restaurant door.

The sign reads
NO SHOES, NO SERVICE

Duty

by Nelson O. Ottenhausen

The young soldier, stationed on guard at a foreign, middle-eastern city street corner, sheltered himself from the biting, late evening wind by standing back against the lee side of a small, one story building. Occasionally, he peered around it to view the large crowd that had gathered out front along the main street. He didn't know why the people were there, nor did he care. After all, it wasn't his country, and he felt it was none of his concern. He had been in the Army for only six months, enlisting on the same day that he had turned eighteen, and had just arrived in country two weeks before. He didn't fully understand, nor did he speak the local language, but he did know a few words and phrases, just enough for him to occasionally sample some of the local food and beverages.

The guard mount commander had instructed him to keep a watch on the crowd, and if they got rowdy and things appeared to be getting out of hand, he should immediately send his buddy stationed across the street for reinforcements at the military garrison, two blocks away. As he looked over the restive crowd, he thought, *It must be a protest for some radical cause or other*.

Occasionally, he thought about home, half a world away, and of a girl named Hannah, whom he planned to marry during his next leave. Six more months and he would be a married man. The thought made him smile.

Suddenly, about a block up the street, the crowd sent up a loud roar, snatching the young soldier away from his marital daydream and back into reality. He quickly stepped away from the building and scanned the area, noticing that many of the people were pointing towards a young woman in the middle of the street. She came from out of the darkness and appeared to float head and shoulders above the crowd, gliding slowly towards where he stood. He saw a bearded man about five steps ahead of the woman, as if he lead the way, pulling her along by some hidden force.

He thought, *Perhaps the woman is sitting on a cart or some other device,* but the soldier couldn't tell because too many people blocked his view. As the couple drew near, he could occasionally see as low as the woman's waist through small gaps between the many bodies in front of him, and she appeared pregnant.

As the shouting got louder, the young soldier became a little concerned for the couple's safety and started to watch the crowd more closely. At the same time, he tried to assess the crowd's mood, but he couldn't determine if it was good or bad because he couldn't understand the language.

He quickly checked his weapons in case he might have to defend himself. Then he turned his attention to a group of five rowdy young men standing nearby, ones that he had seen earlier in the evening drinking alcoholic beverages. He watched them carefully to make sure they didn't throw anything that might cause harm to the passing couple. Soon, the man and woman passed directly in front of the young soldier and the five men, but instead of causing trouble, the drunken five began to cheer and wave their arms over their heads.

Noticing the cheers, the woman turned her head and looked directly at the five men for an instant, then her gaze shifted to the young soldier. Although she smiled when she nodded her head at him, the soldier sensed a brief moment of deep pain and suffering in the woman's eyes. Fascinated by what he saw, he continued to stare at the woman, his eyes locked onto hers by some unknown power. He couldn't tear his gaze away. Within an instant, he thought the woman's face began to emit a subtle, warm and angelic glow. A sudden feeling of inner peace and tranquility swept over him like a wave of water, a feeling he had never experienced before. A moment later, the woman broke eye contact, then she and her male companion proceeded down the street through the crowd and disappeared into the darkness, heading toward one of the local inns.

Within minutes, the crowd became quiet and began to disperse.

After a short while, the young soldier stood his night vigilance alone, the street empty in both directions. He started to go back to the shelter of the building when he noticed three well-dressed men coming out of the darkness from the same direction as the bearded man and pregnant woman had come just moments before, heading directly towards him. At that moment, he heard his commander's voice behind him. "Soldier, you're relieved of your duty here. Fall in."

As he marched back to the barracks in formation with the rest of the sentinels assigned to his detail, the young soldier looked up at the clear dark sky, wondering if the traveling woman with the mournful eyes and peaceful smile had noticed the extremely bright star overhead.

The Sanderling

by Nelson O. Ottenhausen

Late one February afternoon, along Florida's Emerald Coast— we who live here call it Paradise— I was fishing the surf in the Gulf of Mexico off one of the sugar white beaches near Ft. Pickens on the western tip of Santa Rosa Island, when a male Sanderling, a small sparrow like shore bird, landed beside the water's edge about a hundred yards away, then came hopping towards me using only his right leg. The left one, withered below the top joint, was drawn up close to his tiny gray body, swinging uncontrollably at each hop. Although lame, the affliction didn't appear to bother the little bird as he bobbed along like a marionette on a string.

Within minutes, I noticed a gang of laughing gulls beginning to gather around the crippled Sanderling, stretching their necks out while they ran around in tight, crazy-eight circles, flapping their wings and braying their irritating squawks at him. Undaunted, the little bird paid no attention to the raucous gulls and maintained his bouncing one legged pace, stopping periodically to poke his slender bill into the sand, searching for delicacies. When he happened upon a morsel, he would balance himself by spreading his wings outward, throw back his tiny head and quickly eat. Then, ignoring everything around him, he would return to his unwavering purpose, the tedious search for more food.

Before long the little gray bird came nearer, dancing a slalom around three plastic tubes that I had stuck upright on the beach to hold my fishing poles. He continued to peck the sand, spraying grains of it to either side of his wobbly path. Coming within inches from my feet, he displayed no fear at my presence, appearing only to be interested in his foraging. When I stepped back to allow him to pass by, he